BEN

AND HIS

PEN

ISBN# 1-930710-26-7
Copyright ©2000 Veritas Press

Veritas Press
1250 Belle Meade Drive
Lancaster, PA 17601

First edition

BEN
AND HIS
PEN

Words by Emily Fischer
Pictures by Tom Klein

Evan

Veritas Press

This story is dedicated to
my parents who encouraged
me to take up the pen.
—Emily Fischer

When Ben was a lad
he got a pen
from his Pa.

What was this pen for?

Ben was off to
mess with his pen.

The lad was set to
bat with his pen.

But he did not hit
the ball with it.

Ben ran up to
putt with his pen.

But he did not
get the ball in the cup.

Ben was off to hit
a puck with his pen.

But he did not
get it in the net.

All his pen did was put
a mess on his cuff.

In a mad huff,
Ben got rid of his pen.

When Ben was a man
the American men
were upset with
the men in red.

Ben ran to get a pen.
He put in pen a bill.

With this bill
the men from America
and the men in red
were not mad.

Philadᵃ July 5. 1775

Mʳ Strahan,

You are a Member of Parliament, and one of that Majority which has doomed my Country to Destruction. — You have begun to burn our Towns, and murder our People. — Look upon your Hands! — They are stained with the Blood of your Relations! — You and I were long Friends: — You are now my Enemy, — and

I am,

Yours,

B Franklin

The men in red
had to not mess with
the men of America.

By and by red men
and men of Paris
were at the rim
of the American map.

When they set off
to ransack the men of America,
Ben was all mad and
hot in his cap.

But Ben put a lid on it;
he let his pen combat for him.

Ben set in pen to get
bullet and gun for the
men of America.

All the men of America
were set for an attack.

Ben sat back to mull
on his pen.

It did not hit
or bat or putt.

But the pen did not
lack benefit to Ben.

For Ben did a lot
for his kin with his pen.